SOLO PIANO

ESSENTIAL FILM T

THE VERY BEST OF THE LATEST FILM THEMES
BY SOME OF TODAY'S FINEST COMPOSERS

16.95

C000196249

3

Published by
WISE PUBLICATIONS
8/9 Frith Street, London W1D 3JB, UK.

Exclusive Distributors:
MUSIC SALES LIMITED
Distribution Centre, Newmarket Road, Bury St. Edmunds, Suffolk IP33 3YB, UK.
MUSIC SALES PTY LIMITED
120 Rothschild Avenue, Rosebery, NSW 2018, Australia.

Order No. AM985611
ISBN 1-84609-566-2
This book © Copyright 2006 by Wise Publications,
a division of Music Sales Limited.

Unauthorised reproduction of any part of this publication by any means
including photocopying is an infringement of copyright.

Compiled by Nick Crispin.
Arranging and engraving supplied by Camden Music.
Cover design by Fresh Lemon.
Cover photographs courtesy of Rex Features .
Printed in the EU.

Your Guarantee of Quality
As publishers, we strive to produce every book to the highest commercial standards.
This book has been carefully designed to minimise awkward page turns
and to make playing from it a real pleasure.
Particular care has been given to specifying acid-free, neutral-sized paper made
from pulps which have not been elemental chlorine bleached.
This pulp is from farmed sustainable forests and was produced with special regard for the environment.
Throughout, the printing and binding have been planned to ensure a sturdy,
attractive publication which should give years of enjoyment.
If your copy fails to meet our high standards, please inform us and we will gladly replace it.

www.musicsales.com

This publication is not authorised
for sale in the United States of America
and/or Canada.

WISE PUBLICATIONS
part of The Music Sales Group
London/New York/Paris/Sydney/Copenhagen/Berlin/Madrid/Tokyo

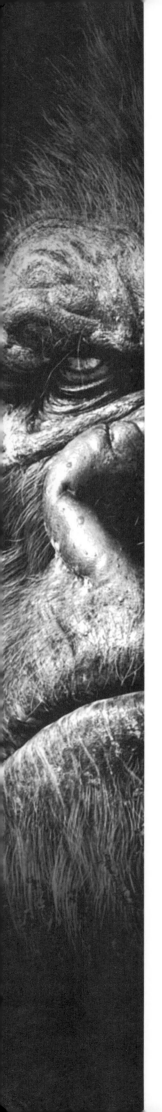

BROKEBACK MOUNTAIN 1

(FROM THE FILM 'BROKEBACK MOUNTAIN')

WORDS & MUSIC BY GUSTAVO SANTOALALLA

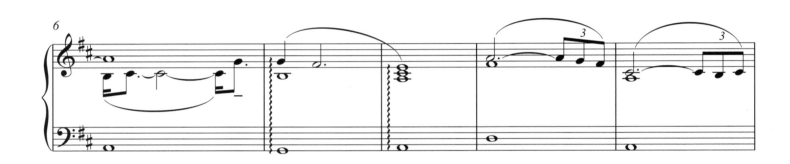

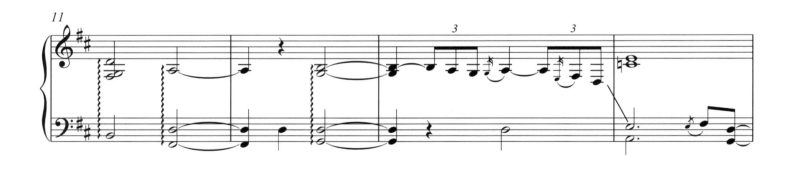

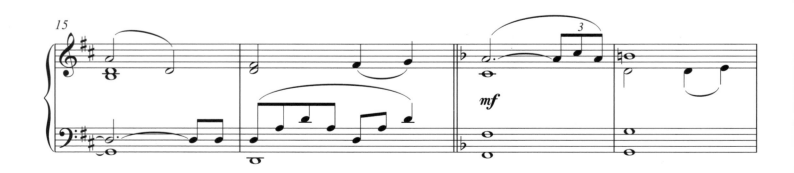

© Copyright 2005 October Cues Music.
Sony/ATV Music Publishing (UK) Limited.
All Rights Reserved. International Copyright Secured.

LUCY MEETS MR TUMNUS

(FROM THE FILM 'THE CHRONICLES OF NARNIA: THE LION, THE WITCH AND THE WARDROBE')

WORDS & MUSIC BY HARRY GREGSON-WILLIAMS

© Copyright 2005 Wonderland Music Company Limited.
Warner/Chappell Artemis Music Limited.
All Rights Reserved. International Copyright Secured.

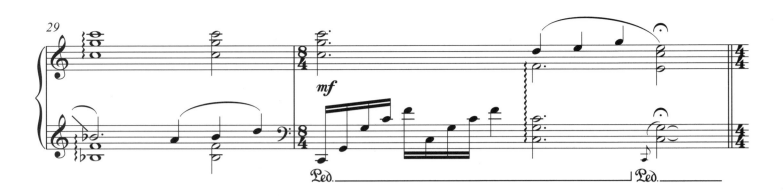

Animato ♩ = c.100

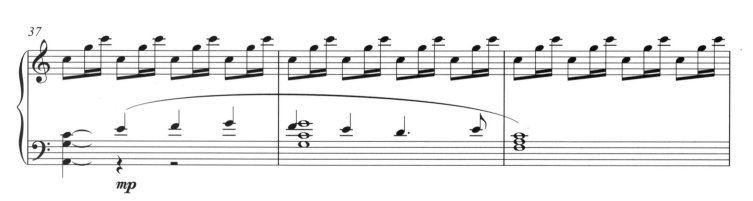

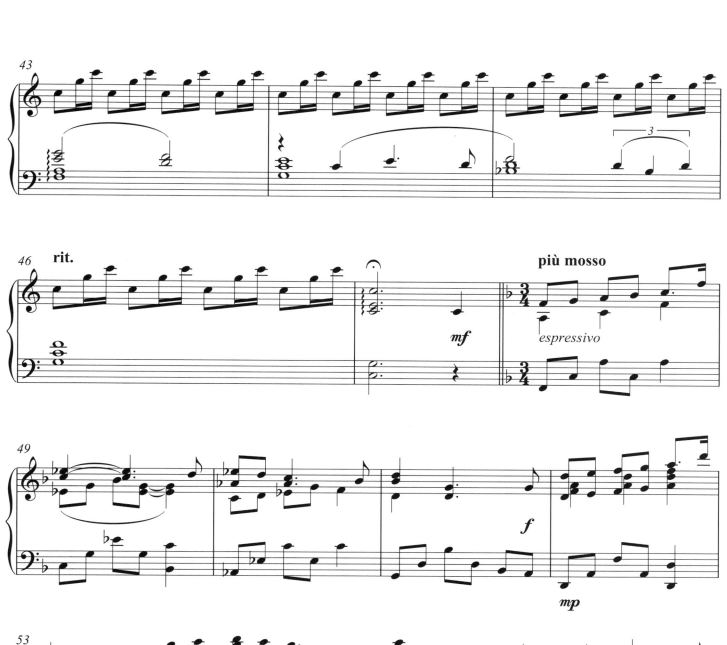

THE INSIDE OUT/CINDERELLA MAN

(FROM THE FILM 'CINDERELLA MAN')

COMPOSED BY THOMAS NEWMAN

© Copyright 2005 UPG Music Publishing.
Universal/MCA Music Limited.
All Rights Reserved. International Copyright Secured.

CINDERELLA MAN

FUNERAL/JUSTIN'S BREAKDOWN/ KOTHBIRO

(FROM THE FILM 'THE CONSTANT GARDENER')
WORDS & MUSIC BY ALBERTO IGLESIAS
'KOTHBIRO' WORDS & MUSIC BY AYUB OGADA

FUNERAL
Slowly and solemnly ♩ = 48

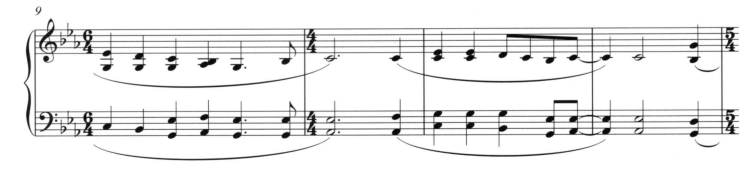

'Funeral/Justin's Breakdown' © Copyright 2005 October Tracks, USA. Sony/ATV Music Publishing (UK) Limited.
All Rights Reserved. International Copyright Secured.
'Kothbiro' © Copyright 2005 Womad Music.
All rights reserved. International Copyright Secured.

JUSTIN'S BREAKDOWN
Very slow and free

poco **f** warm

A tempo ♩ = 48-52

mp

quasi pizz.

KOTHBIRO

Lilting ♩ = 110

THE PARK ON PIANO

(FROM THE FILM 'FINDING NEVERLAND')

MUSIC BY JAN A.P. KACZMAREK

© Copyright 2005 Sony/ATV Music Publishing (UK) Limited.
All Rights Reserved. International Copyright Secured.

24

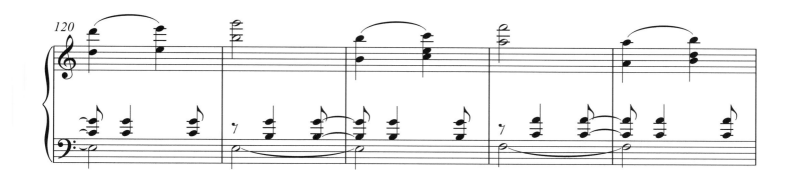

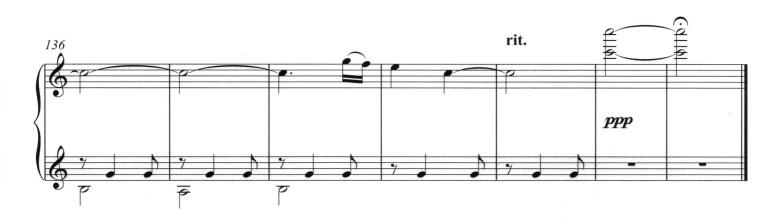

WHERE IS MR BARRIE?

(FROM THE FILM 'FINDING NEVERLAND')

MUSIC BY JAN A.P. KACZMAREK

Allegro con spirito ♩ = 134

© Copyright 2005 Sony/ATV Music Publishing (UK) Limited.
All Rights Reserved. International Copyright Secured.

JB'S BLUES/OMNI/MONDAY (END CREDITS)

(FROM THE FILM 'I ♥ HUCKABEES')

WORDS & MUSIC BY JON BRION

© Copyright 2004 You Can't Take It With You.
Kobalt Music Publishing Limited.
All Rights Reserved. International Copyright Secured.

MONDAY (END CREDITS)

BECOMING A GEISHA/THE CHAIRMAN'S WALTZ

(FROM THE FILM 'MEMOIRS OF A GEISHA')

COMPOSED BY JOHN WILLIAMS

BECOMING A GEISHA

Allegro con moto

© Copyright 2005 Sony/ATV Music Publishing (UK) Limited.
All Rights Reserved. International Copyright Secured.

THE CHAIRMAN'S WALTZ

Andante ma non troppo ♩ = 110

43

OVERTURE/BORED WITH WIDOWHOOD/ PERSUADING TOMMY

(FROM THE FILM 'MRS HENDERSON PRESENTS')

WORDS & MUSIC BY GEORGE FENTON

© Copyright 2005 Shogun Music (75%)/Screen Music Services Limited (25%).
All Rights Reserved. International Copyright Secured.

BORED WITH WIDOWHOOD

PERSUADING TOMMY

In a chamber ensemble style ♩ = 96

HATIKVAH (THE HOPE)/END CREDITS

(FROM THE FILM 'MUNICH')

MUSIC BY JOHN WILLIAMS

© Copyright 2005 Copyright Control (75%)/Cherry Lane Music Limited (25%).
All Rights Reserved. International Copyright Secured.

END CREDITS

Molto rubato

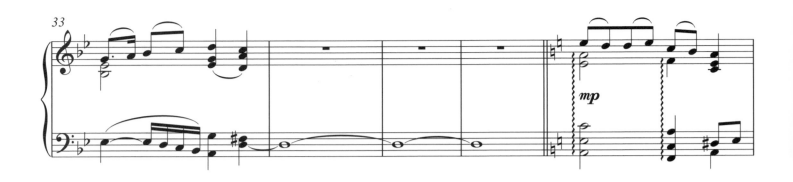

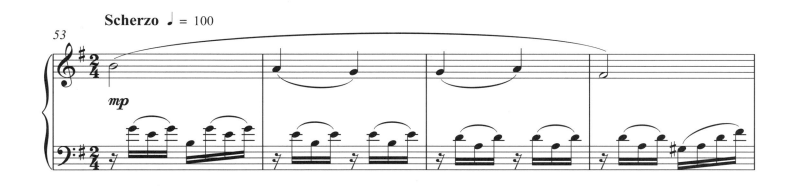

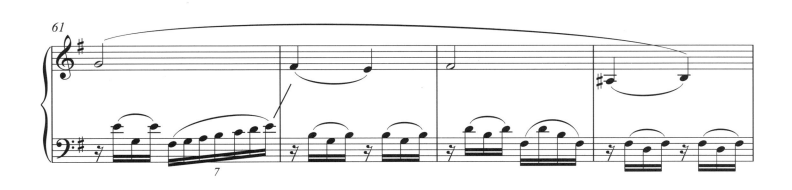

A FATEFUL MEETING/CENTRAL PARK

(FROM THE FILM 'KING KONG')

WORDS & MUSIC BY JAMES NEWTON HOWARD

A FATEFUL MEETING

© Copyright 2005 Universal Music Publishing Limited.
All Rights Reserved. International Copyright Secured.

CENTRAL PARK

THE ROAD TO THE WORKHOUSE

(FROM THE FILM 'OLIVER TWIST')

COMPOSED BY RACHEL PORTMAN

© Copyright 2005 Copyright Control.
All Rights Reserved. International Copyright Secured.

DAWN/GEORGIANA

(FROM THE FILM 'PRIDE AND PREJUDICE')

MUSIC BY DARIO MARIANELLI

DAWN

© Copyright 2005 Universal Music Publishing Limited.
All Rights Reserved. International Copyright Secured.

GEORGIANA

Allegro spirito ♩. = 120

PROOF

(FROM THE FILM 'PROOF')

COMPOSED BY STEPHEN WARBECK

© Copyright 2005 Copyright Control.
All Rights Reserved. International Copyright Secured.

Bringing you the words and the music

All the latest music in print...
rock & pop plus jazz, blues, country,
classical and the best in West End
show scores.

- Books to match your favourite CDs.

- Book-and-CD titles with high quality
  backing tracks for you to play along to.
  Now you can play guitar or piano with your
  favourite artist... or simply sing along!

- Audition songbooks with CD backing
  tracks for both male and female singers
  for all those with stars in their eyes.

- Can't read music? No problem, you can
  still play all the hits with our wide range of
  chord songbooks.

- Check out our range of instrumental
  tutorial titles, taking you from novice to
  expert in no time at all!

- Musical show scores include *The Phantom
  Of The Opera*, *Les Misérables*, *Mamma
  Mia* and many more hit productions.

- DVD master classes featuring the
  techniques of top artists.

Visit your local music shop or, in case of difficulty, contact the Marketing Department,
Music Sales Limited, Newmarket Road, Bury St Edmunds, Suffolk, IP33 3YB, UK
marketing@musicsales.co.uk